Story Clouds

Program Authors
Richard L. Allington
Camille Blachowicz
Ronald L. Cramer
Patricia M. Cunningham
G. Yvonne Pérez
Constance Frazier Robinson
Sam Leaton Sebesta
Richard G. Smith
Robert J. Tierney

Instructional Consultant
John C. Manning

Program Consultants
Nancy Apodaca
Alice Parra

Critic Readers
Elaine K. Cannon
Linda Hassett
Sister Carleen Reck
Norma Rodríguez
Jane Sasaki
Michael M. Sheridan

**Scott, Foresman
and Company**

Editorial Offices:
Glenview, Illinois

Regional Offices:
Sunnyvale, California
Tucker, Georgia
Glenview, Illinois
Oakland, New Jersey
Dallas, Texas

Scott, Foresman Reading: An American Tradition

Acknowledgments

Text
"Clouds" by Christina Rossetti. From *Sing-Song*. The Macmillan Company, Copyright © 1924.

"Jump or Jiggle" by Evelyn Beyer. From *Another Here and Now Story Book* by Lucy Sprague Mitchell. Copyright 1937 by E. P. Dutton, renewed © 1965 by Lucy Sprague Mitchell. Reprinted by permission of the publisher, E. P. Dutton, a division of New American Library.

"The Little Land" by Robert Louis Stevenson

Artists
Reading Warm-up: Eileen Mueller Neill, 6–13; Walt Pozdro, 6–13 (backgrounds)
Section 1: Ted Carr, 16–22; Rick Cooley, 14–15, 52–61, 73; Pat Dypold, 32; Cindy Hoffman, 70; Carl Kock, 23–30, 73; Eileen Mueller Neill, 73; Phil Renaud, 33–42, 73; Slug Signorino, 43–50, 73
Section 2: Len Ebert, 94–102, 103–111; Linda Gist, 84–91; Jackie Rogers, 76–83, 114–119, 120–126
Section 3: Jean Helmer, 168–169; Cindy Hoffman, 170–178; Laura Lydecker, 150–157; Jack Wallen, 180–188

Freelance Photographs
James Ballard 62–69, 74–75, 93, 130–131 (all but top center), 142–148, 184, 187; Ralph Cowan Studio 132–141, 179

Photographs
Page 164: ANIMALS ANIMALS/M. A. Chappell; Page 160: ANIMALS ANIMALS/Patti Murray; Page 161: ANIMALS ANIMALS/Oxford Scientific Films; Page 165: Berg & Assoc./Judy White; Page 143: Centers for Disease Control, Atlanta, GA 30333; Page 158: Earl Kubis/TOM STACK & ASSOCIATES; Pages 162–163: Tom Myers; Page 159: C. Allan Morgan; Page 130 (top center): Runk/Schoenberger from Grant Heilman Photography

Cover Artist
Kinuko Craft

ISBN: 0-673-71506-X

Contents

Stories by:
Caron Lee Cohen
Mary Hynes-Berry
Alice Pasquarella
Liane Onish

Nancy Ross Ryan
Sallie Runck
Mary Shuter
Betty von Glahn

What Is Good for a Crab?

The wind looked down on a boat.

"The fox in the boat can't go," said the wind.
"I will blow to make the boat move."

The wind blew.

Next to the water was a little crab.
The blowing wind gave the crab a fit.

"Say, Wind, up there!" the
crab called.
"The blowing isn't good for me."

The wind saw the little crab on
the ground.

"I wish I could stop blowing," the
wind called down.
"I must blow to make the boat move.
Why don't you go for a swim?
You will like it in the water."

The crab crawled into the water.

"That was good thinking," the crab
said to the wind.
"A swim is fun.
I like being in the water."

The crab was happy.
The wind was happy.
The fox in the boat was happy.

The fun did not last.
The wind saw a very big animal in
the water.
The big animal was a fish.
It was about to reach the crab.

"It is bad for the crab to be next
to that fish," the wind said.
"How can I help the crab?"

The wind looked all about.
He saw a big stick of wood
floating on the water.

Now the crab could see the big,
bad fish.
The crab saw that it had to get out
of the water.

The wind blew the stick.
The wind saw the big stick move.
The stick hit the big, bad fish.
All the fish could do was leave.

The crab said, "Thank you, Wind.
You can blow all you want now.
I can see that a blowing wind can be
good for me."

1

On the Move

Look at some of the
ways we move.
What people move like
animals?
What animals move like
people?

You will read about
many ways we all move.

A Good Day to Sleep

"I can't be late," Chip said.
"I must go to a dog show at school.
Rex will go to the show with me.
But first I'll brush him."

Chip saw the brush on top of a box.
He picked up the brush.
When he picked it up, the box opened.

"Oh no, my cricket box!" Chip said.

First one cricket got out of the box.
Then all eight crickets got out.

"This will make me late," Chip said.
"Today I must be at school at eight."

Chip picked up all eight crickets.
He put the crickets in their box.
Then he went to find Rex.

Chip woke up Rex.
Rex saw the brush and ran out of
the house.
One thing Rex did not like was
to be brushed.

"Rex, we must be at school at eight!"
called Chip.
"I woke up late.
This is the time to get going."

Rex saw a squirrel run next to
Mr. Vega's house.
One thing Rex did not like
was squirrels.

Rex wanted to follow the squirrel.
He ran after the squirrel.

"Rex, don't rush off," Chip said.
"We have no time for this today."

Rex ran after the squirrel.
He rushed into Mr. Vega's paint can.

Mr. Vega came out of the house.

"I came out late," he said to Chip.
"Which animal did this?"

"Rex did it, rushing after the
squirrel," Chip said.
"I'll make all this up to you yet.
Follow me, Rex."

Chip wanted to make Rex take a bath.
One thing Rex did not like was
to take a bath.
So Rex jumped to move from Chip.
Into the water went Chip!

"So much has happened today,"
Chip said.
"I must change for school.
I can't leave yet.
Now I'll be late for the dog show."

Then Chip woke up.
He woke up in the bed.
It was not time for school yet.

"I was sleeping," Chip said to Rex.
"It's a good thing I woke up in time.
We can't be late for the show today.
Let's begin to go to school.
We will get to the show at eight."

Steve Makes a Move

The boys and girls followed Mrs. Sims
out of the school.

"This time we have many things to
do," Mrs. Sims said.
"Let's begin.
What things did you read about in
your reading class today?"

"I can show you," Ted said.
Ted did a hop much like a cricket's.

"Did you read about crickets?" asked
Mrs. Sims.

"No, not yet," said Ted.
"That was a frog following a fly.
It's fun to change into animals."

"I think you came up with a good game today," Mrs. Sims said. "We will call it The Animal Game. You must change to look like animals and move like animals move. Then we will tell which animals we think you are showing. Which one of you wants to begin?"

"I'll change how I look," Pam said.

"You can ride on me and I look like this," Pam said.
She looked very much like a mule.

"We can ride on mules," Steve said.
"Pam, are you a mule?"

"Yes," Pam said.
"We read about how to ride mules."

Lin got down to begin to move much like a duck.

"I think you are a duck!" Steve said.

"Yes," said Lin.
"You are good at this game.
Now it's time for you to change."

"I can't begin yet," he said.
"I want time to think up good moves."

So Rick came right after Lin.
He looked very much like a cat.

"Can we ride on you?" Ted asked.

"No, you can't ride," Rick said.

Then Steve said, "You are a cat!"

"Yes, so you go after me," Rick said.

"Not yet," Steve said.

"Let's see," said Mrs. Sims.
"We saw a frog and a mule.
Which moves came next?
Oh yes, a duck and a cat followed.
Which animal move will Steve make?"

Then Steve said, "I can begin!"
Steve did a little dance.

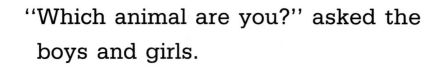

"Which animal are you?" asked the
   boys and girls.

"Are you a pig doing a jig?" Mrs.
   Sims asked.

"No, I am a bear," Steve said.
"We read about bears that dance."

All the children laughed.
It was fun to move like animals.

Checking Comprehension and Skills

Thinking About What You've Read

- **1.** In "A Good Day to Sleep," why does Chip want to be on time for school?

- **2.** What does Chip think Rex did to make him late?

- **3.** In "Steve Makes a Move," why does Steve not want to make a move at first?

  4. Which one of the children is very good at picking out the right animal?
  Why do you think so?

  5. Which of the animals would you have picked to move like?
  Why?

- Comprehension: Details

To be read by the teacher

Jump or Jiggle

by Evelyn Beyer

Frogs jump
Caterpillars hump

Worms wiggle
Bugs jiggle

Rabbits hop
Horses clop

Snakes slide
Seagulls glide

Mice creep
Deer leap

Puppies bounce
Kittens pounce

Lions stalk—
But—
I walk!

The Farmer, the Son, and the Mule

a fable by Aesop
adapted by Mary Hynes-Berry

A farmer wanted to go to the village.

"Follow me, Son," the farmer said.
"Have the mule come after you.
We can ride next to the lake."

"We will reach the lake in no time," said the farmer's son.

So the farmer went first, the son went next, and their mule followed.

Three girls saw the farmer, the son, and the mule.

"Look at that!" said Ella.

"Can you imagine?" laughed Stella.

"What a shame!" said Bella.
"A big mule with nothing on him!
Why can't the boy ride the mule to
the village?"

"Stop!" said the farmer to the mule.
"The others don't like us like this.
We can't stand here all day.
So let us do what the others want.
My son can sit on you."

And so they went.

To Village

Some boys were standing at the lake.
They saw the farmer, the son, and
the mule.

"Can you imagine!" said one boy.
"It's a shame to do such a thing."

"Imagine going to the village in that
way," said the other boy.
"The son rides, but not the farmer."

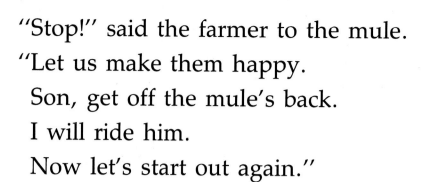

"Stop!" said the farmer to the mule.
"Let us make them happy.
   Son, get off the mule's back.
   I will ride him.
   Now let's start out again."

The farmer sat on the
mule's back.
They started out again.
The mule went in
a mule's slow way.

Some men were at the lake.
They were standing in a line fishing.
They laughed when the three passed.

"Why don't both the farmer and the
boy ride on the back?" the men asked.

"Stop!" the farmer said to the mule.
"My son and I will ride the new way."

Next a man in the lake saw them.

He called out, "For shame, I say!
Imagine such a thing!
Both of you sit on that old mule.
Have you nothing to say about it?
Help the old mule and get off."

"Mule," the farmer started to say,
"let us change to this new way."

"Stop!" said the mule.
"Get down right now.
I can't imagine we can get over to
the village in this way.
Nothing we can do will make all of
them happy.
I'll follow your way of thinking.
Farmer, tell me what you
wish to do."

To Village

"I wish to go home," the farmer said.
"Then we can start over again."

"Good move," the mule said.

So the farmer, the son, and the mule
started out for their home.

Then they went to the village in
their way.

What Squirrel Wants

Bear had new red shoelaces.
Fox had new yellow shoelaces.
Squirrel had old brown shoelaces.
Squirrel did not like her old
brown shoelaces.

"I wish I had new shoelaces like the
others," Squirrel said.

Then one day Squirrel went over to the village and got new shoelaces. They were blue shoelaces.

On the way home, she put them on. She left the old brown shoelaces on the ground.
Then she went to find Bear and Fox.

"Come play a game," Bear called.
"First, stand in back of this line.
Then, we will run over the line and
out to the lake."

"Let's see who will get there first,"
Fox said.

They got in back of the line.
Then off they went.

To Lake

Bear and Fox ran over the line.
So did Squirrel.
Then she had to stop.
Her shoelaces were loose.

"The others got a good start,"
Squirrel said.
"But I have loose shoelaces.
I could fall down in the mud."

A frog called out, "Shame on you!
You can't stand on my bag!"

"Oh!" Squirrel said.

"Look at you!" Frog said.
"A sad squirrel with
loose shoelaces."

"I like your shoelaces," Frog said.

"I don't like them now,"
  Squirrel said.
"They are loose and I can't run."

"What a shame!" Frog said.
"But I can help you start over again.
  Look into my bag of stuff."

"But there is nothing in this bag,"
Squirrel said.

"Nothing?" said Frog.
"Look again, Squirrel."

"Oh, I see my old brown shoelaces!"
Squirrel said.
This time she was happy to see them.

"Take the old brown ones," Frog said.
"They will not get loose.
Then you can run with the others."

Squirrel said, "I will give you the
new, loose shoelaces.
Thank you so much, Frog.
Old shoelaces can be good ones.
Now it's time for me to run!"

Checking Comprehension and Skills

Thinking About What You've Read

1. In "The Farmer, the Son, and the Mule," why does the farmer make so many stops?

2. Was the mule right to make the farmer stop and think?
   Tell what you think.

• 3. Which tells what "What Squirrel Wants" is all about?

   a. Squirrel gets new shoelaces that don't make her happy.

   b. Squirrel puts her old shoelaces on the ground.

• Comprehension: Main idea

How Do We Get There?

"Dad, you and Mom always take us
around town," Ray said.
"One day just Sue and I want to go."

"Right," said Sue.
"We want to find out how to get over
to the big tree.
Then we can see the balloon man."

"I'll tell you what," said their dad.
"I know just the way to help you get
around town.
We will make a picture map.
The pictures will help you get to the
balloon man."

"All right!" said Sue and Ray.
"Let's get started."

Their dad said, "Your first job is
to make a picture of the house."

Sue and Ray did what he said.

"Now let's take a walk," he said.
"We will make pictures of things around
town on the way to the big tree."

They passed their gate on the way
to town.

Then they went down a big hill.
Sue said, "I'll make a picture."

"Good," said their dad.
"You are doing this job well."

"Well, I don't think I am," Ray said.
"Just how can some pictures help us
   reach the big tree?"

"Let's go," was all his dad said.

They walked on and saw Sam's Books.
There were many different books in
Sam's Books.
Many different people were
walking around.

Ray said, "I'll make a picture now.
I know how well we all like books."

"Make the different people too,"
Sue said.

The post office was just next to Sam's Books.

"I'll make a picture of the post office," Sue said.

Then their dad showed them where he wanted to send them next.
Sue and Ray looked over and smiled.
They could see the big tree.

"We are here!" Ray said.
"The balloon man is just over there!"

"You'll get to his balloons," their
dad said.
"First you and Sue must make a
picture of the big tree."

"Not just the tree," said Sue.
"We will show the balloons too."

Ray looked at their picture map and said, "I see the house with the gate. I can see the big hill too."

"Sam's Books is next and then the post office," said Sue. "The last stop is right here."

Their dad said, "Look at the map. "I'll show where we walked. Now nothing is missing."

Ray said, "We have a map from the
house to the balloon man.
I know what we can do now!"

"Well, now just the two of us can get
around town," Sue said.
"We have a map we can follow."

"Good job!" their dad said.

Take a closer look at Ray and Sue's picture map.

A Job at
the Post Office

A **mail carrier** has a big job.
When you send **mail**, a mail carrier
takes it where you want it to go.

Mrs. Jones is a mail carrier.
She starts her day in the
post office.
This is where she gets the mail.

The mail you send goes to the
post office.
Mail carriers like Mrs. Jones look
it over.
First, she has to put some mail here
and some mail there.
Mrs. Jones wants the mail to go to
the right people.

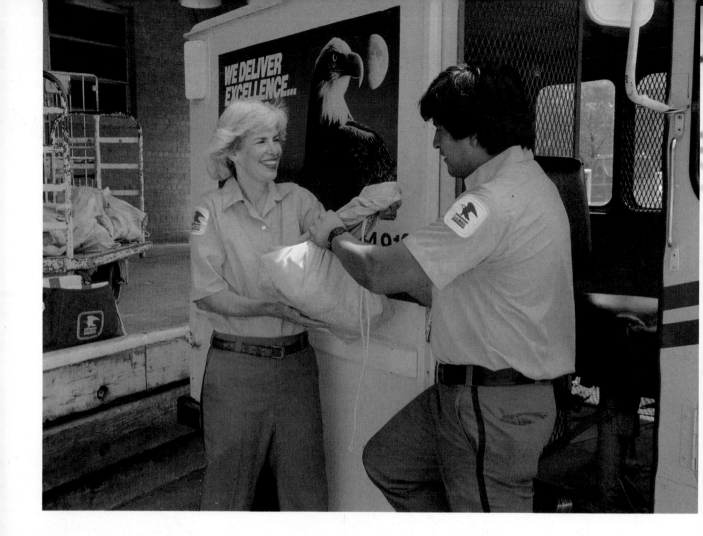

Mrs. Jones puts mail into her bag.
She can't stuff all of the mail into
her bag.
So she gives some of the mail to a
man at the post office.
He will take it to a green **mailbox**.
Mrs. Jones will go to that mailbox
to get mail when she runs out.

A mail carrier takes mail to people
in big and little homes.
Some homes have just one mailbox.
Other homes have many mailboxes.
Mrs. Jones leaves the mail in the
different mailboxes.

You can send boxes to people too.
Mrs. Jones takes just the
little boxes.
Some boxes are too big for her bag.
She gives a little box to a girl at
a gate.

Mrs. Jones is out of mail.
She will get mail from the
green mailbox.
This mailbox has mail just for
mail carriers.

Now she will walk to other homes in
town to leave this mail too.

Mail carriers can help in
different ways.

A man at his gate stops Mrs. Jones.
He is about to move to a new town.
He wants to know how to get mail at
his new home.

Mrs. Jones helps the man at the gate.
She tells him how to let the post
office know where to send his mail.

Now Mrs. Jones is back at the
post office.
She is out of mail.

Mrs. Jones went all around town.
She did much to get the mail out to
other people.
She did her job well.

Mail carriers go all over.
The picture map shows where Mrs.
Jones walked.
Find the picture of the post office.
This is where she started.
Find the green mailbox where she
picked up other mail.
Now find her last stop.

Meet a Reader

Taryn Lynn Stewart, age 7, lives
in Arkansas.

She likes to read at home, sitting
at her desk.
She likes to read at night.

Taryn says, "I like to read, because
it's fun."

Taryn likes make-believe stories.
She also likes stories with lots
of happenings.
The book she likes most is
Doctor De Soto by William Steig.
The book is about a mouse who works
as a dentist.
She thinks it is very funny.

Checking Comprehension and Skills

Thinking About What You've Read

1. Why can't just Ray and Sue go over to the big tree in town?
- 2. How can the picture map help Ray and Sue when just the two of them go to the balloon man?
3. Are Ray and Sue happy with their new map? Why do you think that?
4. Why do you think a mail carrier has a big job?
- 5. The map shows some of the stops of Mrs. Jones the mail carrier. What are they?

• Study Skill: Maps

Thinking About the Section

Who moves for fun?

Who moves to get from here to there?

Who moves to do work?

Who moves to help?

Wind

Farmer

Steve

Mrs. Jones

Ray and Sue

Squirrel

Frog

2

Seeing in Different Ways

What you see may not
always be what
others see.
We all can see things
in different ways.

You will read about
people who see things
one way and then in a
new way.

A Friend You Can't See

My special friend Kim is always at
my side.
What I do, Kim does with me.
The two of us have so much fun.

No one can see Kim but me.

One day Kim and I wanted to draw
an orange.
So I got an orange for both of us.

Mom saw the drawings and said,
"I like your drawing of two oranges.
It looks good, Jan."

"My friend Kim did one drawing," I said.
"She is right here at my side."

"How can that be?" Mom asked.
"I don't see any friend.
I just see your drawing of
two oranges."

One day Mom and Dad said,
"Let's take a bike ride."

Dad said, "This is fun with just
us three."

I said, "Dad, I am on my own special
bike, because Kim is with us."

"But how can that be?" asked Dad.
"Mom and I can't see her."

We left the bikes.
Then we went to a cute place to eat.
I asked for water.

"My friend Kim wants water too,"
I said.

Mom and Dad just looked at me.

"Well, we can't give any water to her,
because we can't see her," Dad said.

One day Mom asked if I would like
to have a pet.
We went to a place to get a pet.
Kim went too.

We saw many cute pets.
I did not know how to pick just one.
Kim said I could pick a fine kitten
as a pet.

We went over to the kittens.
I saw the one I wanted on my own.
Kim and I laughed, because the cute
kitten did some fast moves.

I said, "I'll call her Zap, because
she's so fast.
I'll make her my special friend."

"Good," Mom said and smiled.

So now I have two special friends.
The two friends are all my own.
My friend Kim isn't real.
My kitten Zap is real.
Others can't see Kim, but they all
can see Zap.
Kim is cute and Zap is cute.
Kim will not keep still and Zap will
not keep still.
I'll always want them at my side.
We three are as happy as can be.

I Ride on My Special Side

I ride the train to school.
The ride is no fun for me, because I
don't ride with any friends.
My friends from around my house
go to other schools.

"I don't have any fun on the train,"
I said to Dad one day.

"So ride in a different way today,
Ben," said Dad.
"Think of the side of the train you
sit on as your special side.
Then think up any fun thing
you want."

"It can be fun, Ben," Mom said.
"Do it today on the train."

I got on the train.
The train started to move fast.

"If this were a plane, I could fly,"
I said.

Now my side of the train was special.
I was now flying my own plane.
I had a fine time flying the plane.
I looked at the other side of the
train and it was not a plane.
My ride went very fast.
My side of the train was special.

The next day, I got on the train.
This time the train did not move fast.
This day the train was very slow.

It was time to make my side of the
train special.
I started to think the train was
a big, orange bus.
I could take the bus any place
I wanted to go.
I had a fine ride to school.

The next day, I got on the train,
but the train did not start.
I started to make my side
of the train special.
I started to think I was on
my own bike.
I went as fast as I could.

At last, the train started.
I was just in time for school.

The next day, it looked like rain.
The rain started as I reached
the train.

The rain started me thinking.
I saw all the people as pet fish.
I saw me as a frog in the rain.
I had a fine hop to school.

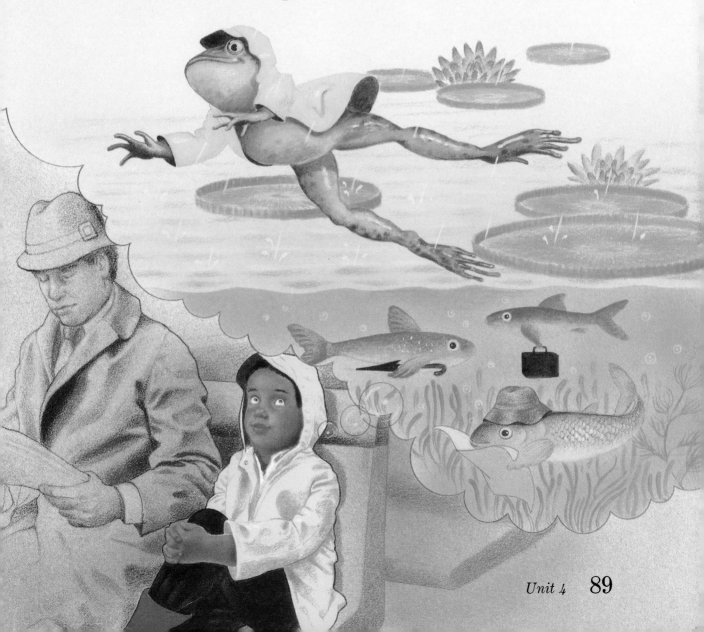

The next day, I got on the train.
I looked out and saw falling snow.

I started to think the snow was a
cloud and that I was on top of it.
It was a fun place to hide.
I could see planes all around.
I could look down and see
my own house.
I floated on the cloud to school.

There was no school the next day.

"My own special side of the train was
  fun!" I said to my mom and dad.
"The train is now a special place.
  I saw the train as a plane.
  Then the train was a bus and a bike.
  One day I was a frog in the rain.
  One day I went to school on a cloud.
  Now my train rides are just fine."

Checking Comprehension and Skills

Thinking About What You've Read

- **1.** What happens when Jan tells her mom that her special friend Kim did one of the drawings?

- **2.** What happens when Jan's mom asks Jan if she would like to have a pet?

   3. Why do you think Jan's mom is happy when Jan says she has a new special friend?

   4. In "I Ride on My Special Side," what happens on the day that Ben's train moves fast?

   5. Do you think Ben has a good way to ride?
   Why do you think as you do?

- Comprehension: Cause and effect

The Little Land
by Robert Louis Stevenson

When at home alone I sit,
And am very tired of it,
I have just to shut my eyes
To go sailing through the skies—
To go sailing far away
To the pleasant Land of Play.

A Meeting with Tall Bear

Miss Wood said to her class one day,
"We will find out more about
the Indians of the past.
First, we will go to a place that
shows all about Indians.
Next, we will see many things that the
Indians of the past did.
Then, we will meet an Indian of today."

The children went with Miss Wood to the special Indian place.

She asked, "Do you know how Indians made their bread?"

"Did they buy it?" asked Manny. "My family buys bread."

Bread

"No, the Indians did not buy bread as your family does," she said.
"Indians of the past made their own. They made their bread outside their houses. As you see, their bread did not look like the bread we buy."

"How did Indians of the past get other things to eat?" Rob asked. "Were they farmers?"

"Yes," said Miss Wood.
"Some Indians were fine farmers.
But they needed rain to grow things.
When they did not get rain, they did a
rain dance outside to try to get it."

"I need to try a rain dance outside,"
said Kris with a grin.
"My flowers always need more rain."

Miss Wood grinned.

"Were there any things the Indians
needed to buy?" asked Manny.

"Indians had to trade for many things
they needed," said Miss Wood.
"Some Indians made pots for drinking water.
They could trade the pots for
things they needed."

"Sometimes Indians wanted fish," she
went on.
"Sometimes they wanted seeds.
Indians could trade pots for them.
Sometimes Indians made pots in the
shapes of animals.
People liked to trade for pots in
the shapes of animals."

"Indians played outside sometimes,"
said Miss Wood.
"They played one game in the snow.
They had to use a stick to play it.
This huge picture shows how an Indian
could play a game called Snow Snake.
He is outside using a stick that is
shaped like a snake."

"It looks like a fine game to play
outside," Cam said with a grin.

Miss Wood said, "Well, we came
to this special place to find out
more about Indians.
We saw how Indians of the past made
and used things.
Now it's time for us to see Tall Bear.
Tall Bear, come meet
my grade one class."

"Tall Bear?" the class asked.

"It's good to see you, class,"
said Tall Bear.
"I am called Tall Bear."

"I am happy you are not a real
bear," said Rob.
"I was about to run away."

All the others grinned.

It's the Way You See It

One day Miss Wood's class went to a special place to find cloud shapes.

"I'll pass out the things you need to use," said Miss Wood. "Try to find shapes in the clouds. Sometimes the clouds will move fast. Try to draw them as well as you can."

"Let your pictures take any shape,"
Miss Wood went on.
"Still, try to do good work.
Draw what you see in the clouds
the way you see it."

The class saw clouds all around.

"Look at that cloud," said Kris.
"It's in the shape of a pig."

"Well, the cloud looks like a sheep to
  me," Manny said.
"It can take any shape we like.
  I think I'll draw the cloud in white."

Just then the wind blew his sheep
cloud away.

Cam said, "Let's try to find more animal shapes.
I see a cloud in the shape of a cat."

"I think it looks more like a sheep," said Manny.
"I'll draw that sheep cloud."

Manny started drawing.
The wind blew the sheep cloud away.

Rob asked, "See that cloud shape?"
"It looks like a dog trying to get
a drink of cold water."

"Yes, it's drinking, but it still
looks like a sheep," said Manny.
"I'll draw a sheep getting a
cold drink."

The drinking sheep cloud blew away.
Manny could not draw it.

"Now there are more clouds all over
  the sky," said Miss Wood.
"I think the sun wants to hide today.
  It's starting to get cold.
  Put on your jackets.
  I don't want you to get too cold."

"The sun is trying to hide," Cam said.
"The wind has made me cold."

"Still, it's fun being outside and
looking for animal shapes," Kris said.
"Look at that huge, black cloud!"

"You know what it looks like?" Manny
asked, grinning.

"We are used to you now," Rob said.
"It looks like a huge, black sheep."

"No, it's more like a can," Manny said.
"It's a huge, black watering can."

"A watering can!" said the others.

They looked up at the huge,
black cloud.
Just then rain came from the cloud.

"You are right!" said Miss Wood.
"It's time for us to go back
to school.
That cloud is a huge, black
watering can!
Let's run!"

The boys and girls ran and laughed.

Checking Comprehension and Skills

Thinking About What You've Read

- **1.** What happens after Miss Wood and her class see the Indian things?

  2. In "A Meeting with Tall Bear," do the boys and girls see things in a different way from Miss Wood?
  Tell why you think as you do.

- **3.** Tell what happens first, next, and last in "It's the Way You See It."

  a. The class rushes away.

  b. The cloud rains on the class.

  c. Miss Wood's class looks at a huge, black cloud.

  4. What animal shapes do you see in clouds?

- Comprehension: Time sequence

Clouds

by Christina Rossetti

ALL: White sheep, white sheep,
On a blue hill,

GIRLS: When the wind stops
You all stand still.

BOYS: When the wind blows
You walk away slow.

ALL: White sheep, white sheep,
Where do you go?

Can You Come Over?

Luis asked his mother to tell him
something he could do for fun.
He was not having fun on his own.
She asked him to go get their mail.

There were three things in their box.
Then Luis saw one other thing.
It was a note from his friends.

The note read, "Can you come over?
Please come to sleep at my house."

"Here's something I can do for fun,"
Luis told his mother.
"This note is from Bret Farmer and
his little brother Sam."

Luis read part of the note to her.

"What a fine little note!" she said.
"But first I must call their mother."

After the call, she told Luis,
"Mrs. Farmer knows about the note.
Bret and his brother want you to come
over today at seven.
Get your things together.
I want your things to be together by
the time I get back."

"I am going to get out some yarn,"
she went on.
"I am taking yarn to Mrs. Farmer."

It got closer to seven.
By that time, Luis saw that he had
almost all his things together.
He wanted to take his new car set.
Many big parts of the car set
would not fit into his bag.

His mother came back.

"I know!" Luis said to her.
"I'll make a special belt.
I'll use it to take two of the seven cars
of the set."

Here's how Luis made the belt.

1. He got some of his mother's yarn.
2. He put yarn on his belt.
3. He put his two cars on the yarn.
4. He put his bag of marbles on
   the yarn too.

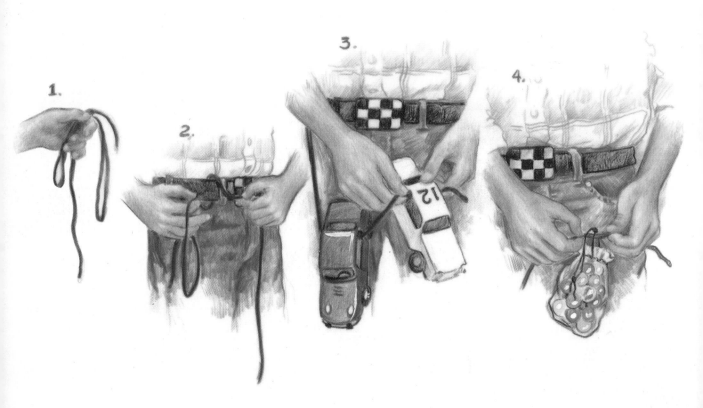

Luis got together six box tops.
He and Bret liked keeping box tops.
He wanted to take one more thing.
It was an ant book for Sam.
Bret's little brother liked ants.

"Zip up your bag and let's go," his
mother called.
"It's almost seven."

A Little Brother Gives More Help

"Thanks for your note," Luis said
  to Bret and Sam.

"I'll thank your mother for the yarn,"
  said Mrs. Farmer.
"Hand over your bag to Bret, Luis.
  You boys had better go play.
  It's almost time for bed."

Luis handed his bag to Bret.
He handed the ant book to Sam.

Bret said, "Now you have six
ant books.
Put it with your five other ant books.
My brother has more books about ants
than he can use.
Sam likes ants more than any other
thing around.
Did you bring the car set, Luis?"

"Not with the tracks," Luis said,
   showing Bret his belt.
"I have something better than that.
   Let's make a car set by using
   this stuff on my belt.
   Your little brother can help us."

"It's no fun having a little brother
   around," Bret told Luis.
"We will let him give us a hand putting
   the parts together."

"I have six box tops," said Luis.
"We may need six more, Bret."

"If you use box tops for tracks, then
  you will need other cars," Sam said.
"The cars you have are not light.
  Why don't you use the marbles in place
  of the cars?"

"Good thinking, Sam," said Luis.
"Give us a hand with the track."

Here's what the boys did to put the
track together.

1. They got many box tops and put
    them on the rug.
2. They put the box tops into the
    shape of a track for cars.
3. They used something to make the
    box tops stick together.

Luis said, "I think the marbles do
make better cars.
The car set is almost made.
I think we need more than this.
I wish we could make the marbles
zip down the track."

Sam said, "Make the marbles move
better by using my six ant books.
Try putting them under the tracks."

Then Luis and Bret put the ant books
under the tracks.

"My brother is something special!"
Bret told Luis.
"Thanks to him, we made a better track
than we could have."

"You know what, Bret?" Luis asked.
"I think you see Sam in a new way.
Having a little brother by your side
can be fun."

Meet a Reader

Zachary Sobel, age 7, lives in
the state of New York.

He likes to read about people
who are not like him.
He likes to read about people doing
exciting things.
He likes funny poetry and books about
animals too.

Zach likes to read on his bed.
He reads next to his bird Gretzky.
Sometimes Zach likes to have his mom
read to him.

Zach says, ''When you're bored, you can
just pick up a book and read it.''

Checking Comprehension and Skills

Thinking About What You've Read

- **1.** What thing does Luis make to take his little cars and marbles to Bret and Sam's?

   2. Bret does not want his little brother Sam around at first.
   Why not?

   3. Does Luis think Bret is right about little brothers?
   Why do you think as you do?

- **4.** In "A Little Brother Gives More Help," what do the boys do first to make the track?

   5. Do you think Sam is happy he helped Luis and Bret?
   Tell why you think as you do.

- Comprehension: Steps in a process

LOOKING BACK

Thinking About the Section

Look at the pictures on the left side.
Then look at the ones on the right.
Tell how the ones on the left side
changed their way of seeing something
on the right side.

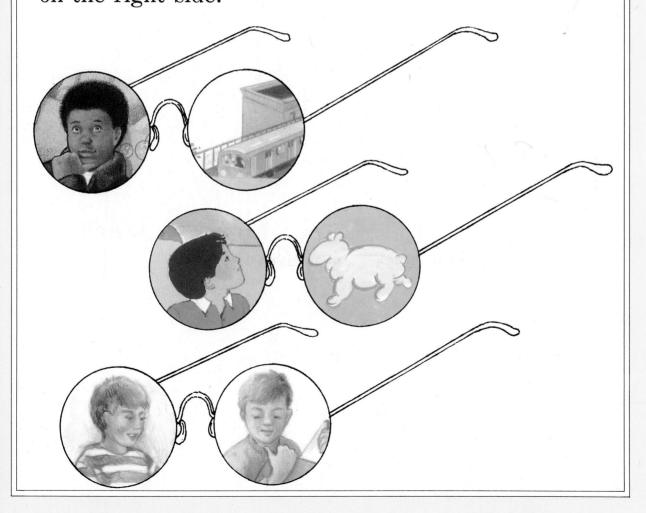

Things We Do

3

Doing What It Takes

There is always
something for us to do.
We do things to live.
We do things to help.
We do things to
be happy.
We do things to make
others happy.

You will read about
some people and animals
who do what it takes.

A Fine Day for Fran
a Swedish folktale adapted by Caron Lee Cohen

Liz | Fran | Sandy | Alice

Dave | Sam | Ed | Pat

Bob | | Beth

LIZ (at FRAN's house):

> A bird was just here!
> I spoke to the bird!
> The bird said nothing, but it left
> four pennies and this note.

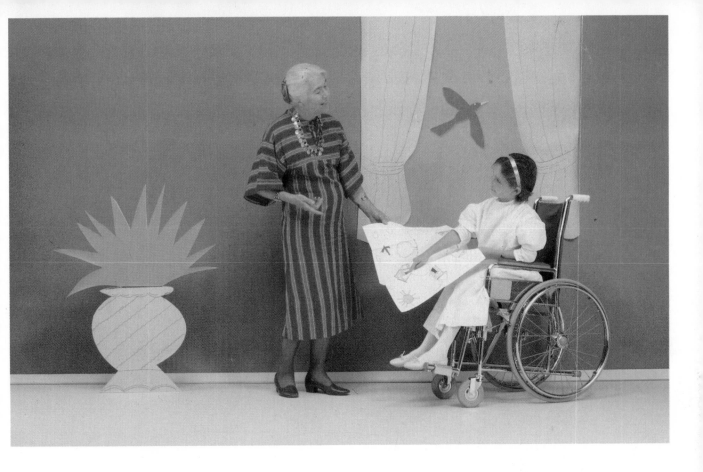

FRAN: Open the note, Liz.
Look, it's a map that tells you
where and how to go!

LIZ (opens map out more): The map
has four rules to follow too.
1. Go when there is no moon, to
   find something fine.
2. Follow the map fast.
3. Look for four doors.
4. Take the four pennies.

FRAN: The bird left its map with you.
Why don't you follow it?
If only I did not have this
cough, I could go with you.

LIZ: It will be fun following the map
and its rules.
I'll find something fine for
you, Fran.
(LIZ **goes away.**)

FRAN (sitting with no one): I wish
the bird had not left its map.
I only wanted Liz and me to
play together.

LIZ (looking at the map and rules):
There is no moon now.
I'll be quick, so Fran will not
miss me.
First, I must find a red door.

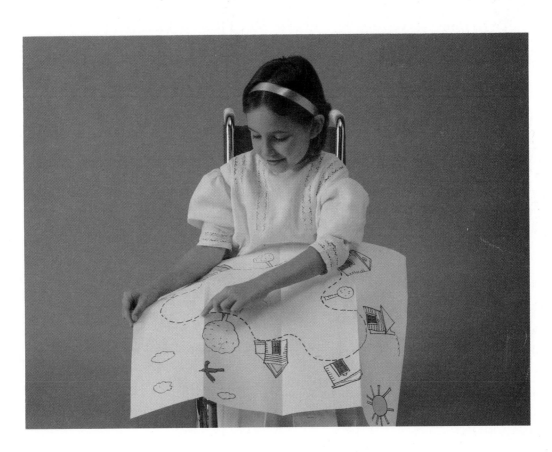

SANDY and **ALICE** **(eating breakfast by**
their red door):
May we help you?

LIZ: My name is Liz and I am
following a map.
My first stop shows a red door.
I want to be quick, so my friend
Fran will not miss me.
I have only four pennies.
I want something fine for Fran.

SANDY: We have nine very fine eggs.
You may have one for only
four pennies.

LIZ: Here are my four pennies.
**(She reaches into her pocket and
shows the pennies.)**

ALICE: Better not put the egg into
your pocket!
If only you had time for
breakfast with us.

(They look on as LIZ goes off.)

LIZ (sees SAM **and** DAVE **eating**
breakfast by their blue door):
My name is Liz and I have
followed a map to your blue door.
I want to be quick, so my friend
Fran will not miss me.
I want something fine for Fran.

SAM and DAVE: Take this breakfast cup.
We'll trade the cup for your egg.

LIZ: I'll put the cup into my pocket.
(She puts cup into her pocket.
She thanks them and goes away.)

**LIZ (sees ED, PAT, and BOB by their
orange door with a book):**
I have followed a map to your
orange door.
I am trying to be quick.
I want something fine for
my friend Fran.

ED and PAT: This book is fine.
It tells about the moon.

BOB: We will trade the moon book
for that cup in your pocket.

(The three trade with LIZ.)

BETH (sitting right next door):
>   If only I had some pennies.
>   I would buy your moon book.

LIZ: The book is yours for no pennies.
>   When I spoke to a bird, it gave
>   me its map.
>   My name is Liz and I followed the
>   map to your white door.
>   I want something fine for
>   my friend Fran.

BETH: Give her this fine day with you!

LIZ: That <u>would</u> be a fine thing!
>   Now I can go back to Fran's.

LIZ (spreading out map at FRAN'S):

    I followed the bird's map, and

    I followed its rules.

    I started with only four pennies.

    I wanted to be quick.

    I spoke to boys and I spoke to girls.

    I traded for fine things.

    Now I know what I can give you.

    Let's share what is left of this

    fine day.

FRAN: That is just what I wanted!

You Can Try to Stop Colds

People cough and sneeze when they
have colds.

This boy has a cold.
He coughs and sneezes.
He does not want to eat breakfast.
He spoke with his mom and dad.
He does not want to take germs
to school.

This is a special picture
of germs.
Germs like the ones
you see here can give
people colds.
You can't see germs
with your eyes.
Many of them could
fit on the tip of a pin!
Germs can get into you.
Then you can get a cold.

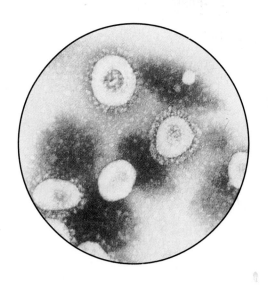

Sometimes you may put your hands on things that have germs.

The germs may get on your hands and into your mouth and eyes.

The germs make you cough.

They make you sneeze.

In almost no time, you are sick!

Germs can spread when you share a glass with a friend.

They can spread when you put the glass to your mouth.

Then, germs can go from your mouth to the glass.

Your friend could get the germs from the glass.

Your friend could get a cold.

Don't share your glass with a friend.

Germs can spread when you cough and
when you sneeze.
They fly out of your mouth.
They go all around you.
A friend who is around when you cough
and sneeze could get your germs.
Your friend could get a cold.
Put your hand over your mouth when
you cough and sneeze.

Know the rules!
Make it your job to keep germs
from spreading.
Don't share things you put into
your mouth.
Put your hand over your mouth when you
cough and sneeze.
The germs will not fly all around
and spread to others.

You still could get a cold sometimes.
By following the rules, you can keep
from getting too many colds.
If you follow the rules, you can help
both you and the people around you.

Checking Comprehension and Skills

Thinking About What You've Read

- **1.** Is Fran happy when Liz goes off to find something to give her? Why do you think as you do?

   2. What is the fine thing Liz gives to Fran?

- **3.** Do you think Fran is happy with what Liz shares with her? Why do you think as you do?

   4. Tell why you think it is good to try to keep away from cold germs.

- **5.** Are germs very little? Why do you think as you do?

- Comprehension: Drawing conclusions

The Cricket and the Ant

a fable by La Fontaine

adapted by Betty von Glahn

I am a cricket that likes to sing.
Singing makes me happy.
I like to sing when I work.
I did not always like to work.
I had to learn to do my share.
I had to learn to be part of a team.
This is the story of how I learned.

One day a team of ants was working.
I was singing as I flew into
the sky.

"It's a fine spring day," I said.
"So why are you ants working?"

"Without work, we can't grow fruit,"
 said one ant.
"Without fruit, we can't eat.
 So why don't you work with us?"

"No, I want to play on this tube
   swing," I said as I flew.
"Come sing and swing."

"You'll be sorry," said the ant.
"You'll be sorry you did not help us."

"I am having too much fun swinging to
   be sorry," I said.

So I played all spring and all fall.

Do you think the cricket will
be sorry?
Why do you think as you do?

In time, the cold winds blew.
The singing birds flew away.
I was without a home.
I was without a thing to eat.
I was without a song to sing.
So I went to a big ant for help.

"What were you doing last spring
when I was working?" she asked.

"I was singing songs," I said.
"I flew on my swing into the sky."

"Oh, you only flew," she said.
"Then, I am not sorry for you."

I said, "But it's snowing outside!"

"Then dance to your songs," she said.
"Play hide and seek with the snow.
That will keep the cold away!"

I walked back to my swing.
I was sorry that I had not worked.
Then someone spoke, and I looked up.

"Mr. Cricket," called a little ant.
"It's too cold for you out here.
Please come home to live with me.
The wind will not sting you there."

I went with the ant to his home.
He made a cup of something hot
for me to drink.
He gave me bread and honey to eat.
I put more into my mouth than ten
crickets could have.

"Why have you helped me?" I asked.

"Your songs are as sweet as honey,"
he told me.
"They made me happy when I worked
in the field."

"Let's work as a team in the field
next spring," I said.
"I'll learn new songs to sing for you,
but this time I'll work as I sing!"

A Working Friend

Think of a **bee.**

Do you think only of a bee **sting?**

Bees do much more than sting people.

In the spring, they make **honey.**

Making honey is a big job.

Sometimes bees sting when someone keeps them from doing that job.

Bees work as a team.

Bees make honey together.

They buzz as they work.

One bee that makes honey is called
a **field bee.**

The field bee can't make honey
without help.

So the field bee teams up with the
house bee.

Field bees work by the flowers.
They like flowers with a sweet smell.
They like flowers that are light
colors better than other flowers.
The field bee gets a sweet drink
from the flowers.
Then, the field bee takes the sweet
drink to the house bee.
The house bee will make honey from
the sweet drink.

Sometimes the field bee finds a very
good set of flowers.
When she goes back to her home, she
does a special dance.
This dance is for other field bees.
It tells them where the flowers are.
When the dance is over, the other
field bees leave.
They fly off to the flowers.
They go to just the right flowers!

The house bee is always working too.
She is always making honey, because
making honey is one of her big jobs.
She does not get much sleep.
So, if she were sleeping and you woke
her, it would not be good.

First, the house bee makes a sheet
of boxes.
All of the boxes have six sides.
Next, she takes the sweet drink from
the field bee.

She puts a little of the sweet drink
into the boxes.
Then, she leaves the boxes open.
In time, the sweet drink in the
boxes changes.

What do you think happens to the drink
in the boxes?
Why do you think as you do?

The sweet drink changes into honey!

People have learned from bees.

We have learned how honey is made.

But there is still more to know.

There are people who work with bees
and know much about them.

See what you can learn from others
who know about bees.

From now on, don't think only of the
bee's sting.

Think of the bee's honey too!

Meet a Reader

Andrea Thompson, age 7, lives
in Oregon.
She knows a quick way to go back
in time.
She just reads a book.
She likes reading books
about dinosaurs.

Andrea reads more than just books.
She reads cereal boxes and comics too.
Andrea also writes.
She reads the stories she writes to
her mom and dad.
Maybe one day you'll read books
by Andrea Thompson!

Checking Comprehension and Skills

Thinking About What You've Read

1. In "The Cricket and the Ant," what do the ants do that the cricket does not want to do?

• 2. Did you think the cricket would be sorry he played all spring and all fall? Why did you think the way you did?

3. In "A Working Friend," what does a field bee do to tell other bees where to find flowers?

• 4. Did you think the sweet drink in the boxes would be honey? What helped you to think the way you did?

5. What is the first thing you think of when you think of bees?

• Comprehension: Predicting outcomes

When Do Bugs Play?

by Nancy Ross Ryan

I went to ask my friends the bugs,
"What did you do today?"
And all the bugs I picked to ask
Had something new to say.

The ant said, "I worked on my hill.
You see that I am working still."

The bees said, "We made honey sweet.
And now it's very good to eat!"

From field to field, the
crickets hopped.
They said, "You see, we just
can't stop!"

A spider said, "Eight hands work fast.
My house is very clean at last!"

"Do you bugs always work?" I asked.
"Don't you have time to play?
How can you look so happy when
you work the day away?"

"We like to work so much," they said.
"We work in rain and sun.
It only looks like work to you,
but we are having fun!"

The Five Pennies

a folk tale adapted by Mary Hynes-Berry

In days past, there was a prince.
He could buy all that he could see.
Still, he was not happy.

One day, this prince was out walking.
He saw a little house.
A man sat with his cat.

"Now then, my sweet little cat,"
  spoke the man.
"There are things we need, you and I.
  I have only five pennies.
  We will go to the village to buy
  the things we need."

"Only five pennies!" said the prince.
"Yet he and his cat are happy.
  It looks as if he has already learned
  a special secret.
  I will follow him and see."

"My little ones are crying to eat,"
  a mother spoke out to the man.
"But I have nothing to cook."

"There is no need to cry," said the man.
  For two pennies, you can buy eggs
  as well as bread and honey."

She and her children thanked him
  for his two pennies.
  He now had only three pennies.

The man and his cat walked to a lake
and saw many fishermen.

A big boy said to them, "I want to be
one of the fishermen.
But I have messed up my fishing line.
I have no way to get a new one."

"Take one of my pennies," said
the man.
"Buy what you need."

The man and his cat went on.
The prince followed.

A little way on, a painter sat.
A friend with caps was at her side.
No one could see the prince hiding.

"Say, what is this?" asked the man.
"Both of you still have work to do.
You need to work on that picture.
You need to work on the caps."

"If only I could," spoke the one with
the caps.

He started to cry.

"I can't use my needle," he went on.
"Who will buy a cap like this?
  I don't have the pennies I need to
  buy a new needle."

"I am no better off than my friend,"
  spoke the painter.
"I need more red paint, but I have
  no pennies to buy it."

Seeing that the two could not go on
made the man and his cat sad.

"They both need one of my pennies,"
  the man spoke to his cat.
"My two pennies will not buy us much.
  We could give them away just as well."

The painter and the man with the caps
  got the last two pennies.

"Well, there are no pennies left," the
  man said with a smile.
"So back we go to the house, my sweet
  little cat."

"Stop!" said the prince with a cry.
"I have followed and looked at you
all day.
You gave all your pennies away.
Are there not things you need?
How can you be happy without
pennies?"

"Oh, we get by, my sweet little cat
and I," the man told him.
"The others need pennies much more
than we do.
Sharing with them makes us happy."

"Well, I'll be!" said the prince.
"You gave to the mother and her
little ones.
You gave to the big boy.
You gave to the painter and the man
with the caps.
Now I see that sharing can make
one happy.
That is something I can learn to do.
Let me begin by sharing what I have
with you."

"Many thanks," said the man.
"We will have more to share with others."

LOOKING BACK

Thinking About the Section

You have read about many who did
something for others.
Look at the pictures at the left.
Then look at the ones at the right.
The people and animals in the pictures
on the left side in some way helped
the ones on the right.
Tell how the ones on the left helped.

Books to Read

School Bus
by Donald Crews

Read this book to find out what school buses do in a day.

And I Mean It, Stanley
by Crosby Bonsall

A little girl makes something very different out of almost nothing.

First Grade Takes a Test
by Miriam Cohen

Find out the special thing a class learns.

Glossary

A a

almost Rosa is almost at school. See the picture.

almost

B b

boat Boats can float on the water. **boats**

breakfast Breakfast is what you eat when you first get up. **breakfasts**

C c

cloud A cloud can hide the sun in the sky.
Some clouds bring rain.
See the picture. **clouds**

cloud

dig

D d

dig The dog is digging into the ground.
See the picture.
digs, digging

door You go into many places by opening a door. **doors**

E e

egg An egg is good to eat. Some people have an egg for breakfast. **eggs**

field

F f

field A field is a place where a farmer can grow things.
See the picture. **fields**

182

G g

glass You can drink from a glass. **glasses**

H h

help Val helps get the leaves. See the picture. **helps, helped, helping**

honey Honey is sweet. Bees make honey from a drink they get from flowers. See the picture.

help

honey

I i

imagine It is fun to imagine you can fly. **imagines, imagined, imagining**

183

J j

just Beth has just come home
from the post office.
See the picture.

just

K k

know

know Mom knows how to make
balloon animals.
See the picture. **knows**

L l

lighthouse The light from
lighthouses shows boats
the way. **lighthouses**
line The people are standing
in line.
See the picture. **lines**

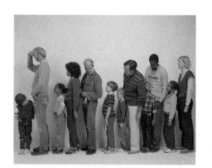

line

M m

map A map is a drawing.
A map helps you find your
way. **maps**

mitten Kenny puts on mittens
to keep his hands from
getting cold.
See the picture. **mittens**

mitten

N n

note A note is a little
letter. **notes**

O o

over Tara jumps over
her brother.
See the picture.

over

185

P p

plane You can fly in a plane.
   planes

Q q

quick

quick James is slow, but Larry
   is quick.
   See the picture.

R r

ride You can ride in the car.

S s

special

special Matt gives Molly a
   special book.
   See the picture.

T t

thank Always thank the ones
who give you help. **thanks,
thanked, thanking**

together Mom and Dad are
jumping together.
See the picture.

together

U u

use The girl uses a straw
to drink.
See the picture. **uses,
used, using**

use

V v

village A village is a little
town. **villages**

wood

W w

wood The box is made of wood.
See the picture.

Y y

yarn

yarn The mittens are made
of yarn.
See the picture.

Z z

zip

zip The boy is zipping up
his jacket.
See the picture. **zips,
zipped, zipping**

Word List

The words listed below are listed by unit. Following each word is the page of the first appearance of the word.